SCHOLASTIC

Maths Practice for

Year 5

Ages 9–10

This book belongs to:

....

SCHOLASTIC

Maths Year 5, Book 1
Book End, Range Road, Witney, Oxfordshire, OX29 0YD
Registered office: Westfield Road, Southam, Warwickshire CV47 0RA
www.scholastic.co.uk

© 2015, Scholastic Ltd

456789 6789012345

British Library Cataloguing-in-Publication Data
A catalogue record for this book is available from the British Library.

ISBN 978-1407-14213-5
Printed in Malaysia

Due to the nature of the web we cannot guarantee the content or links of any site mentioned. We strongly recommend that teachers check websites before using them in the classroom.

Editorial
Rachel Morgan, Robin Hunt, Kate Baxter, Jenny Penfold,
Lucy Tritton, Mark Walker

Design
Scholastic Design Team: Neil Salt, Nicolle Thomas
and Oxford Designers & Illustrators Ltd

Cover Design
Neil Salt

Illustration
Tomek.gr

Contents

Why buy this book?

This series has been designed to support the introduction of the new National Curriculum in schools in England. The new curriculum is more challenging in mathematics and includes the requirement for children's understanding to be secure before moving on. These practice books will help your child revise and practise all of the skills they will learn at school, and including some topics they might not have encountered previously.

How to use this book

- The content is divided into National Curriculum topics (for example, Addition and subtraction, Fractions and so on). Find out what your child is doing in school and dip into the relevant practice activities as required.

- Share the activities and support your child if necessary using the helpful quick tips at the top of most pages.

- Keep the working time short and come back to an activity if your child finds it too difficult. Ask your child to note any areas of difficulty at the back of the book. Don't worry if your child does not 'get' a concept first time, as children learn at different rates and content is likely to be covered throughout the school year.

- Check your child's answers using the answers section at the back of the book.

- Give lots of encouragement and tick off the progress chart as your child completes each chapter.

How to use the book

This tells you which topic you're working on.

This is the title of the activity.

These boxes will help you with the activity.

This is the instruction text. It tells you what to do.

Follow the instruction to complete the activity.

You might have to write on lines, in boxes, draw or circle things.

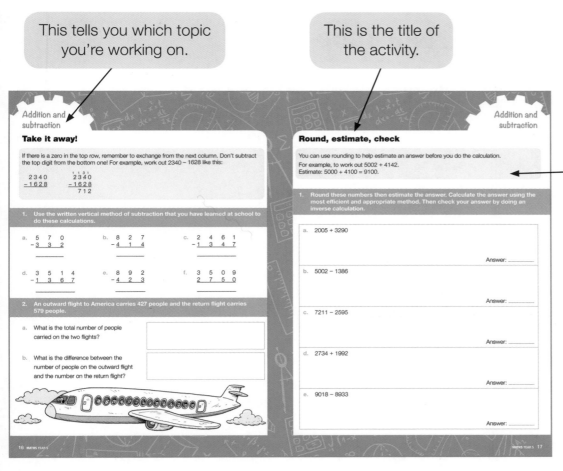

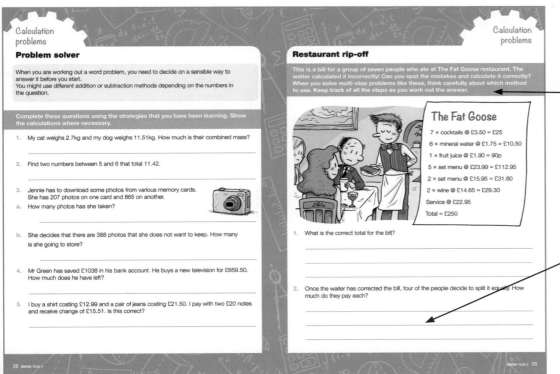

If you need help, ask an adult!

Number and place value

Counting in 10s, 100s and 1000s

Take care when you are counting across the 100s and 1000s.

- Count in 10s: 7**9**5, 8**0**5, 8**1**5…
- Count in 100s: 25,**8**84, 25,**9**84, 26,**0**84…
- Count in 1000s: 9**9**,713, 10**0**,713, 10**1**,713…

1. Count forward in 10s from the number at the start until you reach the number at the end.

a. 812 _822 832 842 852 862 872 882 892_ 902

b. 16,157 _16,167 16,177 16,187 16,197 16,207 16,217_ 16,227

2. Count forward in 100s from the number at the start until you reach the number at the end.

a. 5756 _5,856 5,956 6,056 6,156 6,256 6,356 6456 6,556_ 6656

b. 45,409 _45,509 45,609 45,709 45,809 45,909 46,009_ 46,109

3. Count back in 100s from the number at the start until you reach the number at the end.

a. 36,554 _36,454 36,354 36,254 36,154 36,054 35,954_ 35,854

b. 69,228 _69,128 69,028 68,928 68,828 68,728 68,628_ 68,528

4. Count forward in 1000s from the number at the start until you reach the number at the end.

a. 18,461 _19,461 20,461 21,461 22,461 23,461 24,461_ 25,461

5. Count back in 1000s from the number at the start until you reach the number at the end.

a. 83,753 _82,753 81,753 80,753 79,753 78,753 77,753_ 76,753

Counting with negative numbers

Moving in a positive direction means moving forwards along the number line:

$$-5 \quad -4 \quad -3 \quad -2 \quad -1 \quad 0 \quad 1 \quad 2 \quad 3 \quad 4 \quad 5$$

Moving in a negative direction means moving backwards along the number line:

$$-5 \quad -4 \quad -3 \quad -2 \quad -1 \quad 0 \quad 1 \quad 2 \quad 3 \quad 4 \quad 5$$

$$-10 \ -9 \ -8 \ -7 \ -6 \ -5 \ -4 \ -3 \ -2 \ -1 \ 0 \ 1 \ 2 \ 3 \ 4 \ 5 \ 6 \ 7 \ 8 \ 9 \ 10$$

This is an integer number line.

Numbers on the right-hand side of the line are positive (+) numbers.

Numbers on the left-hand side of the line are negative (–) numbers.

Use the integer number line to help you to solve these problems.

1. Start at −5 and jump eight spaces in a positive direction. Where do you land? ___+3___

2. Start at +3 and jump six spaces in a negative direction. Where do you land? ___-3___

3. Moving in a positive direction, complete these number sequences.

    a. −8, −5, −2, __+1__, __+4__, __+7__, __+10__

    b. −15, −11, −7, __-3__, __+1__, __+5__, __+9__

    c. −24, −19, −14, __+1__, __+6__, __+11__, __+16__

4. Moving in negative direction complete these number sequences.

    a. 15, 10, 5, __0__, __-5__, __-10__, __-15__

    b. 13, 10, 7, __4__, __1__, __-2__, __-5__

    c. 22, 15, 8, 1, __-6__, __-13__, __-20__, __-27__

Reading and writing large numbers

When you write a number, think about what each digit represents.
Watch out for the zeros.
For nine thousand and six, write 9006. The '9' digit is in the 1000s place, so don't write 90006!

1. Write these amounts in figures.

a. forty-three __43__

b. two hundred and seventy-eight __278__

c. five thousand, nine hundred and sixty-one __5,961__

d. twenty-one thousand, six hundred and eighty-three __21,683__

e. four hundred and fifty-seven thousand, nine hundred and thirty-two __457,932__

f. seven thousand and nineteen __7,019__

g. ten thousand and two __10,002__

h. eighty-eight thousand and eight __88,008__

2. Write these amounts in words.

a. 105 __one hundred and five__

b. 150 __one hundred and fifty__

c. 8006 __eight thousand and six__

d. 8060 __eight thousand and sixty__

e. 8600 __eight thousand six hundred__

f. 6008 __six thousand and eight__

Place value in large numbers

When you are working out how many 100s there are in, say, 4516, remember that there are 10 hundreds in 1000. So, 4516 = 45 hundreds + 16.

1. Match the answer to each problem with the same amount in words. The first one has been done for you.

a. 368 + 320 = **688**   One thousand and seventy-two

b. 4290 + 14 = _4,304_   Twenty-four thousand, one hundred and fifty

c. 1472 − 400 = _1,072_   Six hundred and eighty-eight

d. 61,300 + 291 = _61,591_   Sixty-one thousand five hundred and ninety-one

e. 25,000 − 850 = _24,150_   Four thousand, three hundred and four

2. Write down the answer in the first box. In the second box, give the value of the 7 in the answer. The first one has been done for you.

a. 384ml − 9ml = | 375ml | 70ml | b. 443cm + 14cm = | 457cm | 7cm |

c. 758mm + 8mm = | 766 mm | 700mm | d. 990cm − 260cm = | 730cm | 700cm |

e. 1.43m + 5.30m = | 6.73m | 0.70m | f. 7095m + 50m = | 7145m | 7000m |

g. 8020g − 25g = | 7995g | 7000g | h. £4762 − £8 = | £4756 | £ 700 |

3. Give the answers to the following problems in figures.

a. How many tens in three hundred and eighty-seven? _38_

b. How many hundreds in twenty-four thousand and fifty-six? _2400_

c. Which is less: 53 hundreds *or* five thousand, two hundred? _200_

Number and place value

Roman numerals

The Romans wrote numbers using letters.

I = 1   V = 5   X = 10   L = 50   C = 100   D = 500   M = 1000

When a letter comes **after** a larger letter it is added:
VI = V + I = 5 + 1 = 6

When a letter comes **before** a larger letter it is subtracted:
IX = X − I = 10 − 1 = 9

VIII is 5 + 1 + 1 + 1 = 8   LXIV is 50 + 10 + 4 = 64
DL is 500 + 50 = 550   DCCCXC is 500 + 100 + 100 + 100 + 90 = 890

---

1.   Work out these Roman numerals.

a. VII = _____7_____	b. CLIII = _____153_____
c. XIX = _____21_____	d. CIX = _____151_____
e. XXXV = _____35_____	f. DLI = _____551_____
g. XXXVIII = _____38_____	h. DCCX = _____705_____
i. LXX = _____70_____	j. CCCXX = _____320_____
k. MCM = _____2,050_____	l. MDCLV = _____1151_____

Rounding to the nearest 10 and 100

Remember:

- 5**5** rounded to the nearest 10 is 60.   When the 1s digit is 5 or more, round up.
- 8**3** rounded to the nearest 10 is 80.   When the 1s digit is less than 5, round down.
- 5**4**6 rounded to the nearest 100 is 500.   When the 10s digit is less than 5, round down
- 9**8**2 rounded to the nearest 100 is 1000. When the 10s digit is 5 or more, round up.

1. Search for lines of four numbers that round to the same nearest whole 10 or 100. For example, 16, 18, 19 and 21 all round to 20. Colour or circle the lines of numbers that you find.

16	18	19	21	385
894	141	6	204	401
59	60	61	64	399
112	138	912	249	403
897	913	933	935	226
1001	81	78	77	76
999	206	189	177	179
989	167	888	42	214
1004	188	186	194	187
566	581	612	601	26

Addition and subtraction

Pairs and doubles

Choose the best strategy for adding numbers mentally.
Use number facts that you know, such as doubles and bonds to 10 and 100.

1. **Next to each number, write the amount that needs to be added to it to make 50.**

   a. 24 _26_   b. 36 _14_   c. 48 _2_   d. 18 _32_

2. **Write the amount that needs to be added to these numbers to make 100.**

   a. 56 _44_   b. 73 _27_   c. 22 _78_   d. 17 _83_

3. **Answer the question in the units shown.**

   a. 260p + 390p = £ _6.50_   b. 740p + 780p = £ _15.20_

   c. 910cm + 520cm = _1.430_m   d. 830cm + 320cm = _1.250_ m

   e. £2.70 + £9.80 = _12,50_ p   f. £8.70 + £4.40 = _1320_p

4. **Double the first number and then double that answer. There first one has been done for you.**

a.

31	62	124
46	92	184
17	34	68
37	74	148
24	48	96
12	24	48

b.

48	96	192
27	54	108
16	32	64
42	84	168
23	46	92
35	70	140

c.

39	78	156
21	42	84
49	98	196
15	30	60
28	56	112
19	38	76

Adding order

When you add numbers in your head it is often easier to start with the largest number. When there are several small numbers, look for pairs that sum to 10.

$6 + 6 + 14 + 373 + 4 + 4 = 373 + 14 + 6 + 6 + 4 + 4 = 373 + 20 + 10 + 4 = 407$

1.   Rearrange these sums in your head so that you start with the largest amount, then write your answer. Look for number bonds.

a. $7 + 8 + 3 + 115 + 2 + 25 =$ _160_

b. $4 + 3 + 14 + 7 + 6 + 506 =$ _540_

c. $22 + 1 + 748 + 9 + 3 + 7 =$ _790_

d. $5 + 6 + 26 + 5 + 4 + 364 =$ _410_

e. $13 + 2 + 1 + 8 + 9 + 727 =$ _760_

f. $6 + 2 + 17 + 243 + 8 + 4 =$ _280_

g. $2 + 4 + 13 + 8 + 6 + 637 =$ _670_

h. $9 + 8 + 1 + 856 + 2 + 24 =$ _900_

2.   Answer these questions. Remember the rule about putting the largest number first.

a.   The masses of three different crayons are 55g, 65g and 70g. Calculate the total mass of

all three crayons. _55 + 65 = 120   120 + 70 = 190g_
_=10_

b.   Class 1 has seventeen children, Class 2 twenty-four children and Class 3 thirty-six

children. Find the number of children in all three classes. _24 + 36 = 60   60 + 17 = 77_
_17   24   36_

3.   Write a three-number addition using the numbers below. Put the largest number first. Repeat and use a different set of three numbers for each sum. Now work out your sums.

10	65	11	100	35	15	80	20	30	55	33	85	90
95	66	44	110	110	75	99	40	45	5	77	25	88

_95 + 5 = 100   100 + 11 = 111_   _25 + 5 = 30   30 + 20 = 50_

_66 + 44 = 110   110 + 33 = 143_   _45 + 35 = 80   80 + 88 = 168_

Addition and subtraction

Written addition and subtraction

Practise your skills in column addition and subtraction.

```
    7 8 8 5          6 12 1
  + 6 4 2 2        7 3̸ 2 9
  1 4 3 0 7      − 4 5 7 1
      1 1          2 7 5 8
```

Work out these problems using a written calculation method.

a.	4210 + 6709	4 2 1 0 + 6 7 0 9 1 0 9 1 9
b.	2708 + 307	2 7 0 8 + 0 3 0 7 6
c.	1143 + 115	
d.	349 − 164	
e.	8302 − 3408	
f.	8707 − 2819	
g.	4369 + 7098	

Add it!

You can use column addition and subtraction for numbers with more than four digits. Line up the digits and check your working carefully!

```
  37691
+ 66081
 103772
   1   1
```

1. **Use the written vertical method of addition that you have learned to do these calculations.**

a.
```
  57480
+ 60926
```

b.
```
  10245
+    92
```

c.
```
  67553
+ 11101
```

d.
```
  50748
+ 66092
```

e.
```
  87486
+ 10323
```

f.
```
  90067
+ 33908
```

2. **Set these questions out in columns, then work them out.**

a. 52350 + 40031

b. 63174 + 80921

Addition and subtraction

Take it away!

If there is a zero in the top row, remember to exchange from the next column. Don't subtract the top digit from the bottom one! For example, work out 2340 – 1628 like this:

```
  2 3 4 0          ¹ ¹ ³ ¹
- 1 6 2 8          2 3 4 0
                 - 1 6 2 8
                     7 1 2
```

1. **Use the written vertical method of subtraction that you have learned at school to do these calculations.**

a.
```
  5 7 0
- 3 3 2
───────
```

b.
```
  8 2 7
- 4 1 4
───────
```

c.
```
  2 4 6 1
- 1 3 4 7
─────────
```

d.
```
  3 5 1 4
- 1 3 6 7
─────────
```

e.
```
  8 9 2
- 4 2 3
───────
```

f.
```
  3 5 0 9
  2 7 5 0
─────────
```

2. **An outward flight to America carries 427 people and the return flight carries 579 people.**

a. What is the total number of people carried on the two flights?

b. What is the difference between the number of people on the outward flight and the number on the return flight?

Round, estimate, check

You can use rounding to help estimate an answer before you do the calculation.

For example, to work out 5002 + 4142.
Estimate: 5000 + 4100 = 9100.

1. Round these numbers then estimate the answer. Calculate the answer using the most efficient and appropriate method. Then check your answer by doing an inverse calculation.

a. 2005 + 3290

Answer: _____

b. 5002 − 1386

Answer: _____

c. 7211 − 2595

Answer: _____

d. 2734 + 1992

Answer: _____

e. 9018 − 8933

Answer: _____

Multiplication and division

Multiples

A multiple is what you get when you multiply a number by another whole number.
35 is a multiple of 5 and 7 because 5 × 7 = 35.
5 and 7 are factors of 35.

Look at each number. For each one, write as many multiplication facts as you can The first one is done for you.

$2 \times 6 = 12$

12 — $3 \times 4 = 12$

$1 \times 12 = 12$

(81)　　　(30)　　　(48)

(72)　　　(32)　　　(49)　　　(42)

(21)　　　(35)　　　(18)　　　(36)

(56)　　　(64)　　　(63)　　　(27)

(40)　　　(90)　　　(28)　　　(16)

Factor trees

Factor trees are drawn by splitting up numbers into multiplication facts. For example, the factors of 18 are 1, 2, 3, 6, 9 and 18.

Work systematically when you are finding multiplication facts. Use what you know about other numbers to help you. For example, use what you know about multiplication facts for 18 to help you find them for 36.

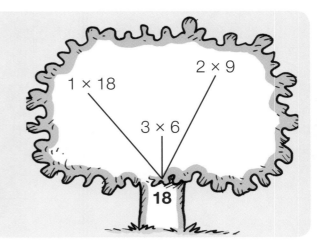

1 × 18

2 × 9

3 × 6

18

---

1. Use the drawings below to make factor trees for the following numbers.

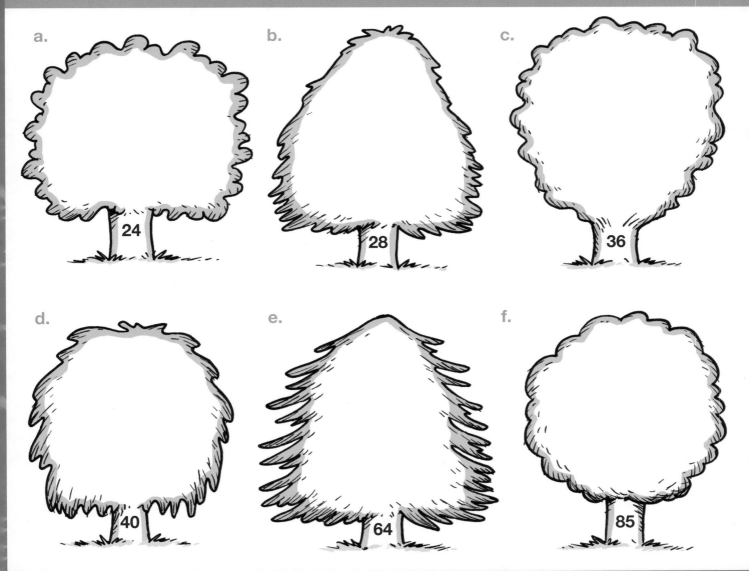

a.

24

b.

28

c.

36

d.

40

e.

64

f.

85

Identify common factors

It helps to look at the largest factors first when you are trying to find a range of common factors.

1. Femi says that he has found all of the factors for 32, the age of his dad. He found four factors. Femi's dad says he is wrong and that there are five factors. Can you find the correct answer?

2. Answer these questions.

a. Find a 2-digit number that has 1, 2, 3, 4, 5 and 6 as factors.

b. Explain why there is only one 2-digit number with this property.

Prime numbers and composite numbers

Composite numbers have more than two factors.
Prime numbers have only two factors, 1 and themselves.

1. Follow the rules to find the prime numbers up to 100. Work systematically.

1. Shade the number 1, as it is not a prime number.
2. Now choose a new colour for shading.
3. Find the first unshaded square.
4. Leave it unshaded, but shade all of its multiples lightly.
5. Return to rule 2 and repeat the process.

1	2	3	4	5	6	7	8	9	10
11	12	13	14	15	16	17	18	19	20
21	22	23	24	25	26	27	28	29	30
31	32	33	34	35	36	37	38	39	40
41	42	43	44	45	46	47	48	49	50
51	52	53	54	55	56	57	58	59	60
61	62	63	64	65	66	67	68	69	70
71	72	73	74	75	76	77	78	79	80
81	82	83	84	85	86	87	88	89	90
91	92	93	94	95	96	97	98	99	100

2. List all the prime numbers up to 100 here.

_____

_____

Multiplication and division

Written multiplication strategies

Here is a reminder of the written column method of short multiplication. Remember to line the digits up correctly.

```
    1 4 2
  ×     7
  ─────────
    9 9 4
    2 1
```

1. Answer these multiplication questions using a written column method.

a. 136 × 4	**b.** 214 × 6
c. 45 × 8	**d.** 54 × 7
e. There were 28 rows of 9 chairs in a school hall. How many people could be seated altogether?	**f.** Cara collected 115 sets of animal stickers. There were 5 stickers in each set. How many individual stickers has she collected?

Divided up

Here is a simple division for 105 ÷ 7 using a written method. As with all written calculations, keep all the columns lined up at all times.

```
    1 5
7 | 1 0 ³5
```
Answer: 15

7 goes into 10 once, with 3 left over.
The 1 is written in the 10s column and the 3 is carried over to the 1s joining with the 5 to make 35.
7 goes into 35 five times with no remainder.
The 5 is written in the 1s column.

1. **Use the written method of division above to work these out.**

a.	b.
6 | 1 5 6	5 | 9 5 5
c. Set this question out yourself. 560 ÷ 4	d. Set this question out yourself. 900 ÷ 6
e. There are 52 children at a party. They need teams of 4 for a game. How many teams can they make?	f. There are 92 balloons in a box. There are four colours of balloon. There is the same number of each colour. How many of each colour are there?

Written division (with remainders)

Here is a simple division for 437 ÷ 5 using a written method:

$$8\ 7\ r\ 2$$
$$5\overline{)4\ 3\ ^37}$$

Answer: 87 remainder 2

5 goes into 43 eight times with 3 left over.
The 8 is written in the 10s column and the 3 is carried over to the 1s joining with the 7 to make 37.
5 goes into 37 seven times with 2 left over. The 7 is written in the 1s column and we write the remainder as r2.

1. **Use a written method to solve these divisions. Remember to write the remainder clearly.**

a.

$$4\overline{)2\ 6\ 7}$$

b.

$$5\overline{)4\ 1\ 7}$$

c.

$$4\overline{)1\ 4\ 5}$$

d.

$$4\overline{)6\ 2\ 5}$$

e.

$$5\overline{)1\ 6\ 7}$$

f.

$$8\overline{)1\ 0\ 7\ 9}$$

Square numbers

A number multiplied by itself makes a square number. 49 is a square number; it can be written as 7×7 or 7^2. All square numbers make a square pattern of squares.

1. **Complete this square number pattern up to 10×10.**

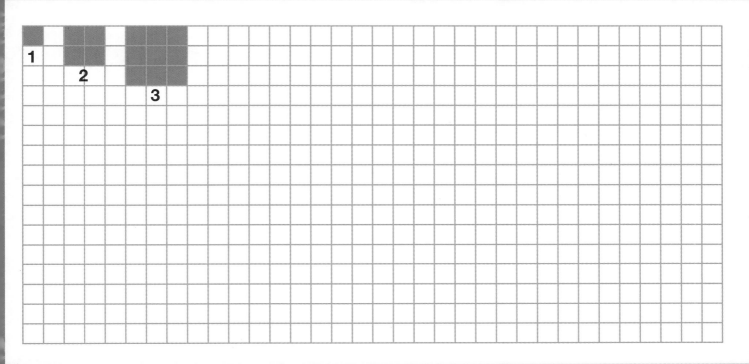

2. **Write out the sequence of square numbers and explore the pattern of differences between these numbers.**

_____

_____

_____

3. **Can you see a relationship? If so, explain what it is. Say how it develops and why.**

_____

_____

_____

Multiplying and dividing by 10, 100 and 1000

When you **multiply** a number by **100**, its digits move **2 places to the left**: 54 × 100 = 5400.

When you **multiply** a number by **1000**, its digits move **3 places to the left**: 54 × 1000 = 54,000.

When you **divide** a number by **100**, its digits move **2 places to the right**: 23,000 ÷ 100 = 230.

When you **divide** a number by **1000**, its digits move **3 places to the right**: 23,000 ÷ 1000 = 23.

1. Make each amount 10, 100 and 1000 times larger.

		× 10	× 100	× 1000
a.	£35		£3500	
b.	12.5m			12,500m
c.	$6\frac{1}{2}$km			
d.	3.45g		345g	
e.	$6\frac{1}{4}$kg			6250kg
f.	4.02g		402g	
g.	$6\frac{3}{4}$m	67.5m		
h.	£0.05			£50.00
i.	0.020g		2g	
j.	$2\frac{1}{2}$km			2500km

2. Underneath each abacus, write in figures the number that is 10 times smaller than the amount shown.

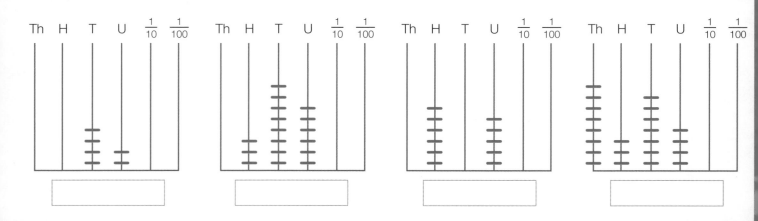

3. Now, on the abacuses below, show the number that is 10 times smaller again than the figure you have just written.

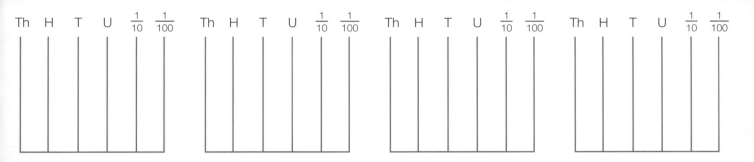

4. Work out these lengths in millimetres, then change the answers first into centimetres and then into metres as shown.

a. 620mm × 2 = | 1240mm | 124cm | 1.24m

b. 6840mm ÷ 2 = | | |

c. 2 × 805mm = | | |

d. 2440mm ÷ 4 = | | |

5. Answer these problems carefully.

a. How many times smaller is 32 than three thousand two hundred? _____

b. Nine pence multiplied by five is _____ times smaller than £4.50.

c. Plastic cups cost £2.50 per 100. Work out the price of 10 cups.

d. How many times smaller is fifty-six than 5600? _____

e. 45,000m is the same distance as _____ kilometres.

Calculation problems

Problem solver

When you are working out a word problem, you need to decide on a sensible way to answer it before you start.
You might use different addition or subtraction methods depending on the numbers in the question.

Complete these questions using the strategies that you have been learning. Show the calculations where necessary.

1. My cat weighs 2.7kg and my dog weighs 11.51kg. How much is their combined mass?

   _____

2. Find two numbers between 5 and 6 that total 11.42.

   _____

3. Jennie has to download some photos from various memory cards.
   She has 207 photos on one card and 865 on another.

   a. How many photos has she taken?

   _____

   b. She decides that there are 388 photos that she does not want to keep. How many is she going to store?

   _____

4. Mr Green has saved £1038 in his bank account. He buys a new television for £659.50. How much does he have left?

   _____

5. I buy a shirt costing £12.99 and a pair of jeans costing £21.50. I pay with two £20 notes and receive change of £15.51. Is this correct?

   _____

Restaurant rip-off

This is a bill for a group of seven people who ate at The Fat Goose restaurant. The waiter calculated it incorrectly! Can you spot the mistakes and calculate it correctly? When you solve multi-step problems like these, think carefully about which method to use. Keep track of all the steps as you work out the answer.

The Fat Goose

7 × cocktails @ £3.50 = £25

6 × mineral water @ £1.75 = £10.50

1 × fruit juice @ £1.90 = 90p

5 × set menu @ £23.99 = £112.95

2 × set menu @ £15.95 = £31.80

2 × wine @ £14.65 = £29.30

Service @ £22.95

Total = £250

1. What is the correct total for the bill?

_____

_____

_____

2. Once the waiter has corrected the bill, four of the people decide to split it equally. How much do they pay each?

_____

_____

_____

Calculation problems

Lots of division

Solve these problems mentally. If you can't do them in your head, use short division to find the answers.

1. Harry has received equal numbers of postcards from 8 different countries. He has received 176 postcards. How many come from each country?

   Answer: _____

2. a. At the zoo, Tariq saw a number of four-legged animals. They had 312 legs between them. He challenged his sister to work out how many animals he had seen that day.

   Answer: _____

   b. Tariq's sister returned the challenge by saying 'If there were 346 visitors and 24 keepers, how many pairs of shoes were there in the zoo that day?'

   Answer: _____

3. A baker packs his cakes into boxes of 6 for the supermarket. He has 255 cakes. How many boxes does he make up? Are there any cakes left for his tea?

   Answer: _____

A sporting problem

1. **Unravel the following information and provide the correct calculations to solve each part of this problem. Work systematically through each question, and write down the steps in order.**

Mr McGee had a problem. There were four different sporting occasions booked for the same day and he had the job of organising the coaches.

- There were only 3 minibuses that could each carry 18 people and 3 large coaches that could each carry 38 people. Two adults must accompany each bus.

- There were 238 children in the school that day. 56 were going to a football tournament; 27 had been invited to the school athletics event in the next town; 18 were swimming in the swimming gala, and 6 had been picked to try their hand at archery.

a. How many children would be left back at school?

_____

_____

b. How many adults would be out on that day?

_____

_____

c. Who should go on which bus?

_____

_____

Compare and order fractions

The **denominator** (bottom number of the fraction) tells you how many equal parts that one whole is divided into.

The **numerator** (top number) tells you how many fractional parts there are. You need to look at **both** parts of all the fractions when you are putting them in order of size.

To order fractions that have different denominators, you may find it easier to first convert all fractions so that they have a common denominator.

1. **Choose a suitable fraction to complete these number sentences.**

a. $\frac{3}{5} >$ [   ]

b. $\frac{3}{4} <$ [   ]

c. $\frac{2}{3} <$ [   ]

d. $\frac{7}{10} >$ [   ]

e. $\frac{5}{8} >$ [   ]

f. $\frac{2}{10} >$ [   ]

g. $\frac{2}{5} <$ [   ]

h. $\frac{6}{10} <$ [   ]

i. $\frac{3}{8} >$ [   ]

j. $\frac{2}{6} <$ [   ]

2. **Convert these fractions to twentieths and then put them in order, starting with the smallest.**

$\frac{3}{5}$ $\frac{15}{20}$ $\frac{7}{10}$ $\frac{2}{10}$ $\frac{2}{4}$ $\frac{2}{5}$ $\frac{8}{10}$ $\frac{1}{4}$

3. **Convert all these fractions to eighteenths and then put them in order, starting with the smallest.**

$\frac{2}{3}$ $\frac{5}{9}$ $\frac{1}{6}$ $\frac{1}{2}$ $\frac{1}{3}$ $\frac{2}{9}$ $\frac{5}{6}$ $\frac{4}{9}$

Equivalent fractions and decimals

The fraction $\frac{1}{10}$ is equivalent to the decimal 0.1.

1. **Draw a line to link each fraction to its equivalent decimal. Use your knowledge of decimals to do this.**

Fractions	Decimals
$\frac{1}{10}$	0.5
$\frac{4}{10}$	0.2
$\frac{1}{5}$	0.9
$\frac{2}{10}$	0.75
$\frac{90}{100}$	0.33
$\frac{1}{2}$	0.2
$\frac{1}{4}$	0.5
$\frac{3}{4}$	0.7
$\frac{5}{10}$	0.3
$\frac{1}{3}$	0.4
$\frac{30}{100}$	0.1
$\frac{70}{100}$	0.25

Improper fractions to mixed numbers

A **mixed number** has a whole-number part and a fraction part: $1\frac{1}{3}$, $4\frac{2}{5}$.

An **improper fraction** has a numerator that is bigger than the denominator: $\frac{5}{3}$, $\frac{7}{2}$.

1. **For each of these diagrams, write their value as an improper fraction and a mixed number. The first one has been done for you.**

a.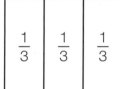

$$\frac{7}{3} = 2\frac{1}{3}$$

b.

_____

c.

_____

d.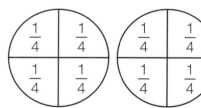

_____

e.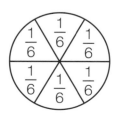

_____

Adding fractions with the same denominator

To add fractions with the same denominator just add the numerators:

$\frac{3}{5} + \frac{4}{5} = \frac{7}{5} = 1\frac{2}{5}$

1. Add across and down to complete the grids. Write the answers as mixed numbers if you need to.

a.

$\frac{4}{5}$	$\frac{3}{5}$	
$\frac{7}{5}$	$\frac{3}{5}$	
	$1\frac{1}{5}$	

b.

$\frac{5}{8}$	$\frac{3}{8}$	
$\frac{7}{8}$	$\frac{3}{8}$	

c.

$\frac{3}{4}$	$\frac{6}{4}$	
$\frac{3}{4}$	$\frac{5}{4}$	

2. Complete the pattern.

a. $\frac{1}{4}$, _____, $1\frac{1}{4}$, _____, _____, $2\frac{3}{4}$, $3\frac{1}{4}$, _____

b. What did you add each time to get the next number? _____

3. Complete the pattern.

a. $\frac{1}{3}$, _____, $1\frac{2}{3}$, $2\frac{1}{3}$, _____, _____

b. What did you add each time to get the next number? _____

Subtracting fractions with the same denominator

To subtract fractions with the same denominator just subtract the numerators:

$\frac{5}{6} - \frac{1}{6} = \frac{4}{6}$

1. **Subtract these fractions.**

a. $\frac{3}{4} - \frac{1}{4} =$ _____

b. $\frac{6}{7} - \frac{3}{7} =$ _____

c. $\frac{9}{10} - \frac{5}{10} =$ _____

d. $1\frac{1}{2} - \frac{1}{2} =$ _____

2. **Subtract across and down to complete the grids. Write the answers as mixed numbers if you need to.**

a.

$\frac{4}{5}$	$\frac{3}{5}$	$\frac{1}{5}$
$\frac{2}{5}$	$\frac{1}{5}$	

b.

$\frac{7}{8}$	$\frac{3}{8}$	
$\frac{4}{8}$	$\frac{3}{8}$	

c.

$\frac{9}{4}$	$\frac{3}{4}$	
$\frac{3}{4}$	$\frac{1}{4}$	

3. **The difference between two fractions is $\frac{1}{2}$. One of the fractions is $\frac{2}{3}$. The other fraction is a proper fraction. What is it?**

_____

Multiplying properly!

$\frac{2}{3} \times 3$ means $\frac{2}{3} + \frac{2}{3} + \frac{2}{3}$. This diagram shows that $\frac{2}{3} + \frac{2}{3} + \frac{2}{3}$ is $\frac{6}{3}$ or 2.

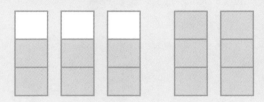

1. Use diagrams to help you work these out.

a. $4 \times \frac{1}{5} = $ _____	b. $\frac{2}{3} \times 5 = $ _____
c. $\frac{2}{3} \times 2 = $ _____	d. $4 \times \frac{2}{3} = $ _____
e. $3 \times \frac{3}{4} = $ _____	f. $\frac{3}{7} \times 5$ _____
g. $4 \times \frac{4}{5} = $ _____	h. $7 \times \frac{1}{3} = $ _____

Decimals: hundredths and thousandths

Each place after the decimal point is a tenth of the value of the place to its left. So the first decimal place is for tenths, the second decimal place is for hundredths and the third decimal place is for thousandths.

10s	1s	.	0.1s	0.01s	0.001s
2	5	.	6	2	3

1. Write the value, in words, of the digit six in each of these numbers. Use the chart above to help you if you need it.

a. 36.775 _____

b. 3.608 _____

c. 21.876 _____

d. 0.462 _____

2. Answer the questions.

a. Which of these numbers is larger than 0.72?

    | 0.712 | | 0.721 |

_____

b. Explain why.

_____

_____

_____

_____

Rounding and ordering decimals

Decimal numbers can be rounded up to lose 'unwanted' digits.
We round up 'halfway' numbers: 32.5 rounds up to 33.
If the first 'unwanted' digit is 5, 6, 7, 8 or 9, add 1 to the last digit that you keep. Then leave off all the unwanted digits. For example:
6.795 rounded to the nearest tenth is 6.8. The 'unwanted' digits are 9 and 5.

A whole number is a non-decimal number.

1. Round these numbers to the nearest whole number.

a. 34.77

b. 765.51

c. 1329.91

2. Round these numbers to the nearest tenth.

a. 34.24

b. 357.76

c. 1546.05

3. Round these numbers to the nearest hundredth.

a. 34.567

b. 109.109

c. 3102.335

4. Order these decimals on the line below, starting from the lowest number.

| 34.40 | 34.09 | 34.43 | 34.092 | 34.015 | 34.323 |

Fractions, decimals and percentages (1)

Percentage means 'per hundred' or 'in every hundred'. Use this fact to change a percentage to a fraction or decimal: 25% means 25 out of every 100, or $\frac{25}{100}$ or 0.25. $\frac{25}{100}$ simplifies to $\frac{1}{4}$.

1. Draw lines to match the fractions, decimals and percentages that are the same.

$\frac{1}{10}$ 20%   0.5 $\frac{1}{4}$

0.25   0.1   75%   50%

10% $\frac{2}{10}$ $\frac{3}{10}$ 0.3   25%

30%   0.2 $\frac{1}{2}$ $\frac{3}{4}$ 0.75

2. When you have matched all six sets, rewrite each percentage as a fraction with a denominator of 100, and as a decimal, as in the example below.

$10\% = \frac{10}{100} = 0.1$

Fractions, decimals and percentages (2)

To change a decimal to a percentage, multiply it by 100.
So, 0.45 as a percentage is 0.45 × 100% = 45%
To find 50% halve the number. To find 10%, divide by 10.

1. Draw lines to link the equivalent decimals, fractions and percentages. One trio has been joined up for you.

0.1	$\frac{2}{10}$	60%
0.2	$\frac{7}{10}$	80%
0.3	$\frac{8}{10}$	90%
0.4	$\frac{1}{10}$	70%
0.5	$\frac{6}{10}$	40%
0.6	$\frac{3}{10}$	50%
0.7	$\frac{9}{10}$	30%
0.8	$\frac{4}{10}$	10%
0.9	$\frac{5}{10}$	20%

2. Draw lines to link the matching amounts. One trio has been joined up for you.

$\frac{1}{2}$ of 30	6	75% of 16
$\frac{1}{4}$ of 80	12	25% of 80
$\frac{1}{5}$ of 35	3	40% of 45
$\frac{3}{4}$ of 16	20	20% of 35
$\frac{1}{10}$ of 60	15	10% of 60
$\frac{1}{3}$ of 9	18	$33\frac{1}{3}$% of 9
$\frac{2}{5}$ of 45	7	50% of 30

Measuring and converting lengths

To convert centimetres to millimetres multiply by 10.

To convert metres to centimetres multiply by 100.

To convert metres to millimetres multiply by 1000.

To convert millimetres to centimetres divide by 10.

To convert centimetres to metres divide by 100.

To convert millimetres to metres divide by 1000.

1. **First estimate and then measure the following items. Express your measurements in the suggested units. Then choose three more things to measure and write them in the table.**

Length of your garden or building		cm	m
Width of lounge		cm	m
Length of dining table		cm	m
Height of your chair		cm	mm

Converting mass

Remember, there are 1000 grams in a kilogram.

Multiply by 1000 to convert kilograms to grams.

Divide by 1000 to convert grams to kilograms.

Mrs Jones has parcels to send to Australia for her nieces and nephews. She has three empty parcel boxes but each has a maximum weight restriction.

1. Here are the packages that she wants to send. Help her to decide which packages may be sent in which box.

Measurement

Metric and imperial length problems

Imperial measurements were originally linked to parts of the body. For example, an inch was the width of a man's thumb at the knuckle. People still use imperial measures as well as metric ones; they might say their mass in stones and pounds rather than kilograms, or their height in feet and inches rather than metres and centimetres.

1. **Use the chart to help you work out the answers to these problems. The first one has been done for you.**

Length

Imperial to metric	Metric to imperial
1 inch (in) = 2.54cm	1cm ≈ 0.4 inch
1 foot (ft) ≈ 30cm	1m ≈ 40 inches
1 yard (yd) ≈ 90cm	1km ≈ 0.6 miles
1 mile ≈ 1.6km	

a. Dwayne throws a cricket ball 10 yards.
How many centimetres does he throw the cricket ball?

10 × 90cm = 900cm. The cricket ball went 900cm.

b. Shanee throws the cricket ball twice as far as Dwayne.
How far does she throw the ball? Answer in metres.

_____

c. Nat's hair is 5 inches longer than her mum's. Her mum's hair is 30cm long.
How many centimetres long is Nat's hair?

_____

d. Keira is 5 feet tall. Her brother Josh is 40cm taller.
How tall is Josh in metres and centimetres?

_____

Perimeter

Perimeter is the distance around the outside of a shape. You can use what you know about shapes to find their perimeter without using a ruler to measure every side. For example, a square has four sides of equal length.

1. Measure the sides of each shape (in centimetres) and work out its perimeter.

a.

Perimeter _____

b.

Perimeter _____

c.

Perimeter _____

d.

Perimeter _____

e.

Perimeter _____

Finding areas

You can find the area of a shape by counting squares on paper or by calculating.
For a rectangle, the formula is area = length × width.
For example, 6cm × 2cm = 12cm² Don't forget the ² which means *squared*.

1. **Find the area of these shapes. Look carefully at the units of measurement: you will need to convert some of them.**

1.
6cm

4cm

2.
8m

5m

4.
10cm

0.8m

5.
80cm

0.3m

3.
0.7m

20cm

6.

0.6m

40cm

	Area
1.	
2.	
3.	
4.	
5.	
6.	

Estimate volume

You can find the volume of cubes and cuboids by counting the number of layers and the number of cubes in each layer.

1. **Use small cubes to build two larger cubes and record their volumes.**

   _____ cube units   _____ cube units

2. **Use small cubes to build two cuboids and record their volumes.**

   _____ cube units   _____ cube units

3. **Look at Jon's cube. How many more cubes are needed to make Holly's cube?**

_____ cubes

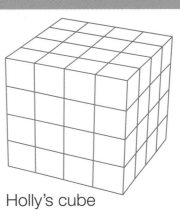

Jon's cube   Holly's cube

4. **In these diagrams there are no cubes you can't see unless they are needed to hold up another cube.**

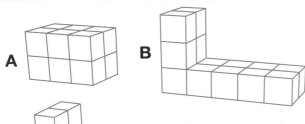

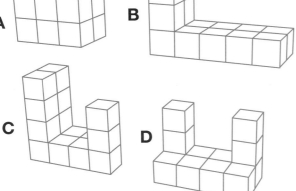

   a. Which two shapes have the same

      volume? _____

   b. What is their volume?

      _____ cube units

Estimate capacity

There are 1000 millilitres (ml) in a litre (l). Smaller capacities are measured in millilitres. Larger capacities are measured in litres.

Take five different-sized containers and a litre measuring jug. Label the containers A to E.

- Look at the litre jug. Compare with container A and make an estimate of its capacity. Record it in the table.
- Fill container A with sand or water and use the measuring jug to find out how much it actually holds. Record the result.
- Do the same for all the containers B to E.

Container	Estimate	Capacity
A		
B		
C		
D		
E		

1. Which of your estimates was best? Container _____

2. Which estimate wasn't so good? Container _____

3. Why did you find it hard to make a good estimate of the capacity of this container?

_____

_____

Activities diary

When you add times, remember that there are 60 minutes in an hour. You could use a blank time line to help if you need to.

1. Keep a diary for 24 hours of the activities given below. Use the recording chart to help. Remember that you may do some things more than once a day.

2. Calculate the time you spent doing these things in a day.
   How long do you think you would spend on them over a week or a month or a year?
   Write these in the table, using an appropriate unit of time.

   For example, if you spend 55 minutes playing football and play three times a week, you would spend 2 hours 45 minutes ((3 × 55 mins) ÷ 60) a week playing football, or 11 hours ((4 × 165 mins) ÷ 60) a month, and 132 hours or $5\frac{1}{2}$ days a year (12 × 11 hours = 132 hours, 132 ÷ 24 = $5\frac{1}{2}$ days).

3. Choose your own activities to add to the table.

Activity	Time	Time spent	Total for 24 hours	Week	Month	Year
Playing football	11:15 – 12:10	55 mins	55 mins	2h 45	11 hours	$5\frac{1}{2}$ days
Sleeping						
Eating						
Washing/ bathing						
Exercising						
Watching TV/using computer						

Geometry: properties of shapes

Acute, obtuse or right?

An angle is a measure of turn. There are 360° in one whole turn.

An acute angle is less than 90°.	An obtuse angle is more than 90°, but less than 180°.	A right angle is exactly 90°.

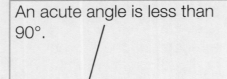

1. Label each of these angles either acute, obtuse or a right angle.

a. _____

b. _____

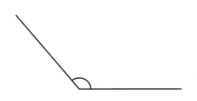

c. _____

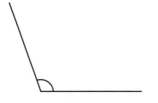

d. _____

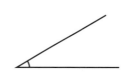

e. _____

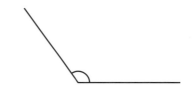

f. _____

g. _____

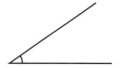

h. _____

i. _____

What's the angle?

When you measure an angle:

- First estimate its size, or decide if it acute, obtuse or a right angle.
- Line up your protractor correctly.
- Use the correct scale on the protractor.

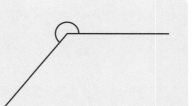

1. Look closely at these angles. Use your set square or protractor to label them as acute, obtuse or right angles.

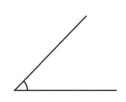  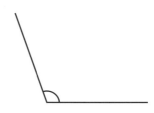 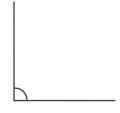

a. _____ b. _____ c. _____ d. _____

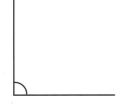  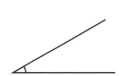 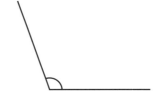

e. _____ f. _____ g. _____ h. _____

2. Use your protractor to measure these angles as carefully as you can and label them.

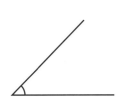 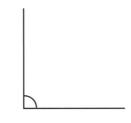 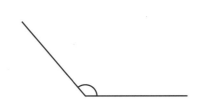

a. _____ b. _____ c. _____

Shape nets

To work out which nets are correct, choose the base first, then imagine the other faces folded up around it.

Look at these 3D shapes. Next to each shape are two possible nets. However, only one of the nets will form that particular shape. Identify the correct net for each 3D shape, and mark it with a tick.

1. 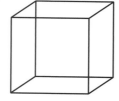 a.  b.

2.  a.  b.

3. 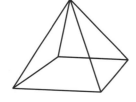 a. 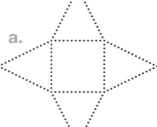 b.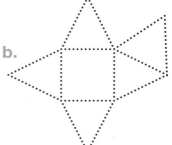

4.  a. b.

Find what's missing

You can use what you know about the properties of shapes to help you find missing lengths and angles.

1. Draw a rectangle with sides 3cm and 6cm long. Then draw, measure and label the diagonals. Measure and label the angles where the diagonals cross.
2. Repeat the same steps for a square with sides 4cm long.

3. **What have you discovered about the angles between the diagonals of a square?**

_____

4. **Diagram ABCD shows a rectangle.**

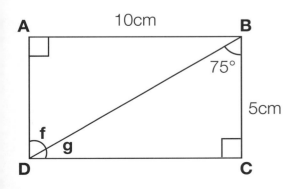

a. What is the size of angle *g*? _____

b. What is the length of side AD? _____

c. What is the length of side DC? _____

Reflect it!

When you reflect a shape in a mirror line, the matching points of the object and image are the same distance from the line. The size and shape of the object and image are exactly the same.

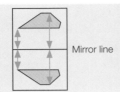

Mirror line

1. Reflect the shapes in both mirror lines. Remember to number each reflected point A1, B1, C1, A2, B2, C2 and so on.

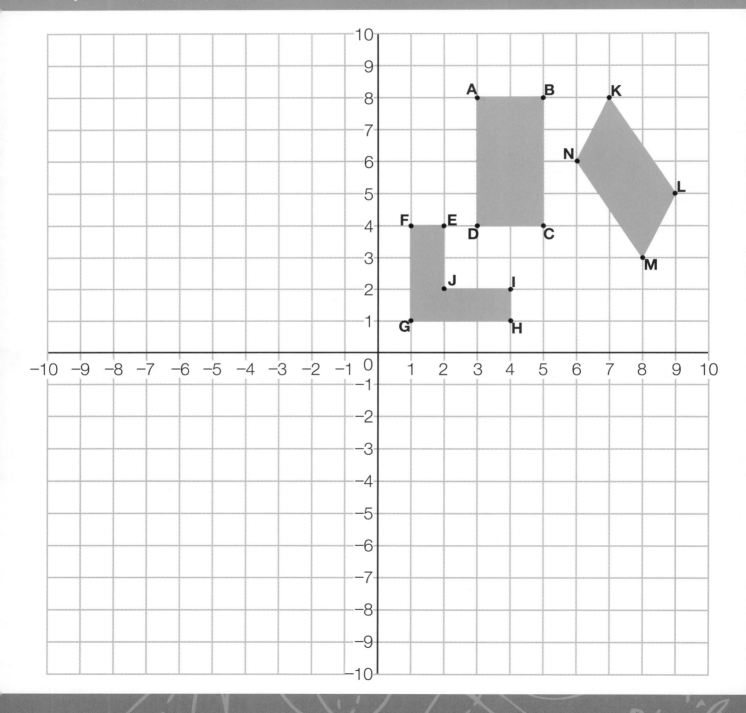

Translate and reflect

When you translate an object:

- Every point of the object moves the same distance in the same direction.
- The image is the same size and shape as the object.

1. Write the coordinates of the points A, B, C, D and E.

   A _____   B _____   C _____

   D _____   E _____

2. Join the points to make a shape. Translate the shape eight squares to the left.

3. Then reflect the new shape in the horizontal mirror line.

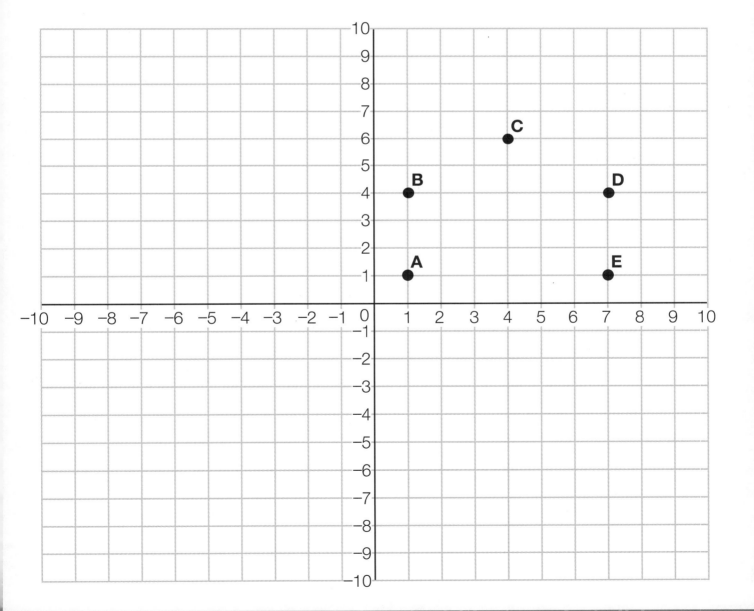

Comparing data

A line graph is a useful way of showing changes over time.
Before you answer questions about a line graph, look at the graph and make sure you understand what it is showing. Look at the title and labels. Make sure you understand the scale.

Look at these two line graphs. They show the temperatures in London and Athens over one 12-hour period in summer.
Use the graphs to answer the questions below.

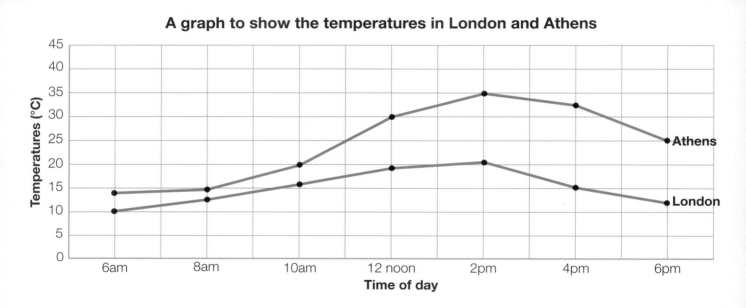

A graph to show the temperatures in London and Athens

1. What is the difference between the highest temperatures shown in Athens and London?

    _____

2. What is the difference between the highest and lowest temperatures in London?

    _____

3. What is the temperature in each city at 5:00pm? _____

4. Why is this information displayed as a line graph, not a bar chart or a bar line graph?

    _____

    _____

    _____

Line graph problems

Remember to read the times and numbers on each axis carefully when you enter the data on to a graph.

The petrol in the tank of a lorry was measured every hour. These are the measurements. Input this information on to the line graph below.

Time	10:00	11:00	12:00	13:00	14:00	15:00
Volume of petrol	50 litres	30 litres	20 litres	20 litres	5 litres 50 litres	35 litres

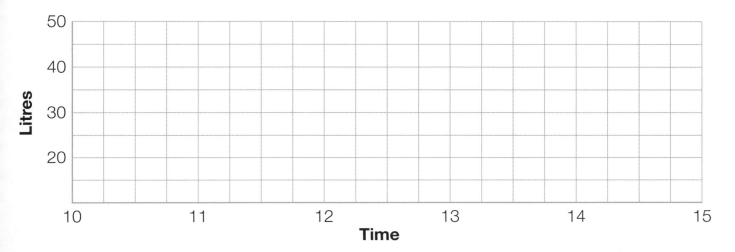

Now use the graph to answer these questions.

1. How much petrol was in the tank at 11:30? _____

2. At approximately what time was the petrol at 10 litres? _____

3. What do you think happened between 12:00 and 13:00? (Check how much petrol was used and why that might be.)

_____

4. What happened at 14:00? _____

5. How much petrol was used in the last hour of the journey? _____

Complete a timetable

To work out a time interval, count on from the start time to the end time. You could use a blank time line to help you.

Here is part of a timetable which is being considered for trains between Norwich and Liverpool. Study it carefully and then try to answer the questions below.

Norwich							12.52	13.49	a.	15.53	16.57	18.45	19.30	20.51
Thetford							13.19	14.16	b.	16.20	17.24	19.12	19.57	21.18
Ely							13.49	14.47	c.	f.	17.51	19.46	20.22	21.46
Peterborough							14.28	15.25	d.	17.15	18.30	20.25	20.55	22.20
Grantham							14.57	15.58	e.	17.49	19.05	21.00	n.	22.55
Nottingham	09.12	10.36	11.45	12.35	13.33	14.38	15.34	16.44	17.32	18.33	19.45	21.40	22.10	23.35
Chesterfield	09.52	11.13	12.20	13.17	14.17	15.16	16.16	17.20	18.12	19.13	20.15	l.		
Sheffield	10.15	11.37	12.39	13.37	14.37	15.35	16.36	17.42	18.35	19.25	20.35	j.		
Stockport	11.22	12.24	13.25	14.23	15.33	16.23	17.23	18.26	19.23	20.23	21.17	k.		
Manchester Piccadilly	11.37	12.37	13.37	14.37	15.37	16.37	17.37	18.37	19.37	20.32	21.28	l.		
Liverpool Lime Street	12.22	14.25	14.25	15.24	16.25	17.25	18.25	19.25	20.25	g.	h.	m.		

1. How long does the first train from Nottingham take to reach Liverpool Lime Street?

_____

_____

2. What is the shortest journey time from Nottingham to Liverpool Lime Street?

_____

_____

3. Use the times between stations to complete this section of the return journey from Liverpool Lime Street to Nottingham.

Liverpool Lime Street	12.00
Manchester Piccadilly	
Stockport	
Sheffield	
Chesterfield	
Nottingham	

4. There is a proposal to extend the train service. The boxes with letters on the timetable on the previous page represent when the extended service will run. Use other entries in the timetable to estimate suitable times for the new service. Write your estimates below.

a. _____

b. _____

c. _____

d. _____

e. _____

f. _____

g. _____

h. _____

i. _____

j. _____

k. _____

l. _____

m. _____

n. _____

Jay wants to travel by train from Exeter to meet the 15.37 at Manchester Piccadilly. Use the internet to find the times and details of his best journey.

Progress chart

Making progress? Tick (✔) the cogs as you complete each section of the book.

	Most questions completed	All questions completed
Number and place value	○	○
More practice?		
Addition and subtraction	○	○
More practice?		
Multiplication and division	○	○
More practice?		
Calculation problems	○	○
More practice?		
Fractions, decimals and percentages	○	○
More practice?		
Measurement	○	○
More practice?		
Geometry: properties of shapes	○	○
More practice?		
Geometry: position and direction	○	○
More practice?		
Statistics	○	○
More practice?		

Answers

The answers are given below. They are referenced by page number and where applicable, question number. The answers usually only include the information the children are expected to give.

Page number	Question number	Answers
6	1a	822, 832, 842, 852, 862, 872, 882, 892
	1b	16,167, 16,177, 16,187, 16,197, 16,207, 16,217
	2a	5856, 5956, 6056, 6156, 6256, 6356, 6456, 6556
	2b	45,509, 45,609, 45,709, 45,809, 45,909, 46,009
	3a	36,454, 36,354, 36,254, 36,154, 36,054, 35,954
	3b	69,128, 69,028, 68,928, 68,828, 68,728, 68,628
	4a	19,461, 20,461, 21,461, 22,461, 23,461, 24,461
	5a	82,753, 81,753, 80,753, 79,753, 78,753, 77,753
7	1	3
	2	−3
	3a	1, 4, 7, 10.
	3b	−3, 1, 5, 9
	3c	−9, −4, 1, 6
	4a	0, −5, −10, −15
	4b	4, 1, −2, −5
	4c	−6, −13, −20, −27
8	1a	43
	1b	278
	1c	5,961
	1d	21,683
	1e	457,932
	1f	7,019
	1g	10,002
	1h	88,008
	2a	One hundred and five
	2b	One hundred and fifty
	2c	Eight thousand and six
	2d	Eight thousand and sixty
	2e	Eight thousand, six hundred
	2f	Six thousand and eight
9	1b	4304 = Four thousand, three hundred and four
	1c	1072 = One thousand and seventy-two
	1d	61,591 = Sixty-one thousand, five hundred and ninety-one
	1e	24,150 = Twenty-four thousand, one hundred and fifty
	2b	457cm; 7cm
	2c	766mm; 700mm
	2d	730cm; 700cm
	2e	6.73m; 0.7m or 70cm
	2f	7145m; 7000m
	2g	7995g; 7000g
	2h	£4754; £700
	3a	38
	3b	240
	3c	Five thousand, two hundred
10	1a	7
	1b	153
	1c	19
	1d	109
	1e	35

Page number	Question number	Answers
10	1f	551
	1g	38
	1h	710
	1i	70
	1j	320
	1k	1900
	1l	1655
11	1	Nearest 10: 59, 60, 61, 64 81, 78, 77, 76 Nearest 100: 897, 913, 933, 935 385, 401, 399, 403 206, 189, 177, 179 188, 186, 194, 187 566, 581, 612, 601 1001, 999, 989, 1004
12	1a	26
	1b	14
	1c	2
	1d	32
	2a	44
	2b	27
	2c	78
	2d	83
	3a	£6.50
	3b	£15.20
	3c	14.3m
	3d	11.5m
	3e	1250p
	3f	1310p

Page 12, Question 4a:

46	92	184
17	34	68
37	74	148
24	48	96
12	24	48

Page 12, Question 4b:

48	96	192
27	54	108
16	32	64
42	84	168
23	46	92
35	70	140

Page 12, Question 4c:

39	78	156
21	42	84
49	98	196
15	30	60
28	56	112
19	38	76

Page number	Question number	Answers
13	1a	160
	1b	540
	1c	790
	1d	410
	1e	760
	1f	280
	1g	670
	1h	900
	2a	70g + 65g + 55g = 190g
	2b	36 + 24 + 17 = 77 children
	3	Answers will vary.
14	a	10,919
	b	3015
	c	1258
	d	185
	e	4894
	f	5888
	g	11,467
15	1a	118,406
	1b	10,337
	1c	78,654
	1d	116,840
	1e	97,809
	1f	123,975
	2a	52350 + 40031 92381
	2b	63174 + 80921 144095
16	1a	238
	1b	413
	1c	1114
	1d	2147
	1e	469
	1f	759
	2a	1006
	2b	152
17	1a	2000 + 3000 = 5000 2005 + 3290 = 5295 5295 − 2005 = 3290
	1b	5000 − 1400 = 3600 5002 − 1386 = 3616 3616 + 1386 = 5002
	1c	7200 − 2500 = 4700 7211 − 2595 = 4616 4616 + 2595 = 7211
	1d	3000 + 2000 = 5000 2734 + 1992 = 4726 4726 − 1992 = 2734
	1e	9000 − 9000 = 0 9018 − 8933 = 85 8933 + 85 = 9018
18		81: 9 × 9, 3 × 27, 1 × 81 30: 1 × 30, 2 × 15, 3 × 10, 5 × 6 48: 1 × 48, 2 × 24, 3 × 16, 4 × 12, 8 × 6 72: 1 × 72, 2 × 36, 3 × 24, 4 × 18, 6 × 12, 8 × 9 32: 1 × 32, 2 × 16, 4 × 8 49: 1 × 49, 7 × 7 42: 1 × 42, 2 × 21, 3 × 14, 6 × 7 21: 1 × 21, 3 × 7 35: 1 × 35, 5 × 7 18: 1 × 18, 2 × 9, 3 × 6 36: 1 × 36, 2 × 18, 3 × 12, 4 × 9, 6 × 6 56: 1 × 56, 2 × 28, 4 × 14, 7 × 8

Page number	Question number	Answers
18		64: 1 × 64, 2 × 32, 4 × 16, 8 × 8 63: 1 × 63, 3 × 21, 7 × 9 27: 1 × 27, 3 × 9 40: 1 × 40, 2 × 20, 4 × 10, 5 × 8 90: 1 × 90, 2 × 45, 3 × 30, 5 × 18, 6 × 15, 9 × 10 28: 1 × 28, 2 × 14, 4 × 7 16: 1 × 16, 2 × 8, 4 × 4
19	1a	1 × 24, 2 × 12, 3 × 8, 4 × 6
	1b	1 × 28, 2 × 14, 4 × 7
	1c	1 × 36, 2 × 18, 3 × 12, 4 × 9, 6 × 6
	1d	1 × 40, 2 × 20, 4 × 10, 5 × 8
	1e	1 × 64, 2 × 32, 4 × 16, 8 × 8
	1f	1 × 85, 5 × 17
20	1	There are 6 factors 1, 2, 4, 8, 16, 32
	2a	60
	2b	Because there is no other number under 100 that can be divided by all those numbers and give a whole number answer.
21	1	Check children's answers.
	2	The prime numbers less than 100 are: 2, 3, 5, 7, 11, 13, 17, 23, 29, 31, 37, 41, 43, 47, 53, 59, 61, 67, 71, 73, 79, 83, 89, 97
22	1a	544
	1b	1284
	1c	360
	1d	378
	1e	252
	1f	575
23	1a	26
	1b	191
	1c	140
	1d	150
	1e	13
	1f	23
24	1a	66 r3
	1b	83 r2
	1c	36 r1
	1d	156 r1
	1e	33 r2
	1f	134 r7
25	1	
	2	1, 2, 4, 9, 16, 25, 36, 49, 64, 81, 100
	3	Answers will vary.

26–27 1

		×10	×100	×1000
a.	£35	£350	£3500	£35,000
b.	12.5m	125m	1250m	12,500m
c.	$6\frac{1}{2}$ km	65km	650km	6500km
d.	3.45g	34.5g	345g	3450g
e.	$6\frac{1}{4}$ kg	62.5	625kg	6250kg
f.	4.02g	40.2g	402g	4020g
g.	$6\frac{3}{4}$ m	67.5m	675m	6750m
h.	£0.05	£0.50	£5.00	£50.00
i.	0.020g	0.2g	2g	20g
j.	$2\frac{1}{2}$ km	25km	250km	2500km

Page number	Question number	Answers
	2	4.2, 38.6, 60.5, 837.4
	3	Abacus shows 0.42, 3.86, 6.05, 83.74
	4b	3420mm, 342cm, 3.42m
	4c	1610mm, 161cm, 1.61m
	4d	610mm, 61cm, 0.61m
	5a	100 times
	5b	10
	5c	25p
	5d	100
	5e	45
28	1	14.21kg
	2	Answers will vary. For example, 5.49, 5.93
	3a	1072
	3b	684
	4	£378.50
	5	No, I should receive £5.51
29	1	No, it should be £24.50 + £10.50 + £1.90 + £119.95 + £31.90 + £29.30 + £22.95 = £241.00
	2	£241 ÷ 4 = £60.25
30	1	22
	2a	78
	2b	370 pairs
	3	42 boxes, 3 left for his tea
31	1a	131 children
	1b	12 adults
	1c	Football (2 coaches); Athletics (1 coach); Swimming (2 minibuses); Archery (minibus)
32	1a	Answers will vary. For example, $\frac{1}{5}$
	1b	Answers will vary. For example, $\frac{7}{8}$
	1c	Answers will vary. For example, $\frac{5}{6}$
	1d	Answers will vary. For example, $\frac{1}{10}$
	1e	Answers will vary. For example, $\frac{1}{8}$
	1f	Answers will vary. For example, $\frac{1}{10}$
	1g	Answers will vary. For example, $\frac{3}{5}$
	1h	Answers will vary. For example, $\frac{7}{10}$
	1i	Answers will vary. For example, $\frac{1}{8}$
	1j	Answers will vary. For example, $\frac{3}{6}$
	2	$\frac{2}{10}, \frac{1}{4}, \frac{3}{5}, \frac{7}{10}, \frac{15}{20}, \frac{8}{10}$
	3	$\frac{1}{6}, \frac{2}{9}, \frac{1}{3}, \frac{4}{9}, \frac{1}{2}, \frac{5}{9}, \frac{2}{3}, \frac{5}{6}$
33	1	$\frac{1}{10} = 0.1$ $\frac{1}{4} = 0.25$ $\frac{4}{10} = 0.4$ $\frac{3}{4} = 0.25$ $\frac{1}{5} = 0.2$ $\frac{5}{10} = 0.5$ $\frac{2}{10} = 0.2$ $\frac{1}{3} = 0.33$ $\frac{90}{100} = 0.9$ $\frac{30}{100} = 0.3$ $\frac{1}{2} = 0.5$ $\frac{70}{100} = 0.7$
34	1b	$\frac{17}{5} = 3\frac{2}{5}$
	1c	$\frac{9}{2} = 4\frac{1}{2}$
	1d	$\frac{9}{4} = 2\frac{1}{4}$
	1e	$\frac{7}{6} = 1\frac{1}{6}$

	1a	
$\frac{4}{5}$	$\frac{3}{5}$	$1\frac{2}{5}$
$\frac{7}{5}$	$\frac{3}{5}$	2
$2\frac{1}{5}$	$1\frac{1}{5}$	

	1b	
$\frac{5}{8}$	$\frac{3}{8}$	1
$\frac{7}{8}$	$\frac{3}{8}$	$1\frac{1}{4}$
$1\frac{1}{2}$	$\frac{6}{8}$	

Page number	Question number	Answers
	1c	

$\frac{3}{4}$	$\frac{6}{4}$	$2\frac{1}{4}$
$\frac{3}{4}$	$\frac{5}{4}$	2
$1\frac{1}{2}$	$2\frac{3}{4}$	

Page number	Question number	Answers
	2a	$\frac{1}{4}, \frac{3}{4}, 1\frac{1}{4}, 1\frac{3}{4}, 2\frac{1}{4}, 2\frac{3}{4}, 3\frac{1}{4}, 3\frac{3}{4}$
	2b	$\frac{2}{4}$ or $\frac{1}{2}$
	3a	$\frac{1}{3}, 1, 1\frac{2}{3}, 2\frac{1}{3}, 3, 3\frac{2}{3}$
	3b	$\frac{2}{3}$
36	1a	$\frac{2}{4}$ or $\frac{1}{2}$
	1b	$\frac{3}{7}$
	1c	$\frac{4}{10}$ or $\frac{2}{5}$
	1d	1

	2a	
$\frac{4}{5}$	$\frac{3}{5}$	$\frac{1}{5}$
$\frac{2}{5}$	$\frac{1}{5}$	$\frac{1}{5}$
$\frac{2}{5}$	$\frac{2}{5}$	

	2b	
$\frac{7}{8}$	$\frac{3}{8}$	$\frac{3}{8}$ or $\frac{1}{2}$
$\frac{4}{8}$	$\frac{3}{8}$	$\frac{1}{8}$
$\frac{3}{8}$	0	

	2c	
$\frac{9}{4}$	$\frac{3}{4}$	$1\frac{1}{2}$
$\frac{3}{4}$	$\frac{1}{4}$	$\frac{2}{4}$ or $\frac{1}{2}$
$1\frac{1}{2}$	$\frac{2}{4}$ or $\frac{1}{2}$	

Page number	Question number	Answers
	3	1/6
37	1a	$\frac{4}{5}$
	1b	$\frac{10}{3}$ or $3\frac{1}{3}$
	1c	$\frac{4}{3}$ or $1\frac{1}{3}$
	1d	$\frac{8}{3}$ or $2\frac{2}{3}$
	1e	$\frac{9}{4}$ or $2\frac{1}{4}$
	1f	$\frac{15}{7}$ or $2\frac{1}{7}$
	1g	$\frac{16}{5}$ or $3\frac{1}{5}$
	1h	$\frac{7}{3}$ or $2\frac{1}{3}$
38	1a	Six units
	1b	Six tenths
	1c	Six thousandths
	1d	Six hundredths
	2a	0.721
	2b	0.72 has a zero in the thousandths column whereas 0.721 has a 1 in the thousandths column making it larger.
39	1a	35
	1b	766
	1c	1330
	2a	34.2
	2b	357.8
	2c	1546.1
	3a	34.57
	3b	109.11
	3c	3102.34
	4	34.015, 34.09, 34.092, 34.323, 34.40, 34.43

Page number	Question number	Answers
40	1	1/10, 0.1, 10% 3/10, 0.3, 30% 2/10, 0.2, 20% 1/2, 0.5, 50% 1/4, 0.25, 25% 3/4, 0.75, 75%
	2	20% = 20/100 = 0.2 50% = 50/100 = 0.5 25% = 25/100 = 0.25 75% = 75/100 = 0.75 30% = 30/100 = 0.3
41	1	0.2, 2/10, 20% 0.6, 6/10, 60% 0.3, 3/10, 30% 0.7, 7/10, 70% 0.4, 4/10, 40% 0.8, 8/10, 80% 0.5, 5/10, 50% 0.9, 9/10, 90%
	2	1/2 of 30, 15, 50% of 30 1/10 of 60, 6, 10% of 60 1/4 of 80, 20, 25% of 80 1/3 of 9, 3, 33 1/3% of 9 1/5 of 35, 7, 20% of 35 3/4 of 16, 12, 75% of 16 2/5 of 45, 18, 40% of 45
42	1	Answers will vary, check children's accuracy.
43	1	Answers may vary, for example: 5kg + 2.5kg + 250g in Max 8kg box 1390g + 800g + 780g in Max 5kg box 4kg + 3980g in Max 8kg box
44	1b	18m
	1c	Nat's hair is 43.18cm long
	1d	1m 90cm
45	1a	8.8cm
	1b	8.8cm
	1c	7.8cm
	1d	9.3cm
	1e	16cm
46	1	1: Area = 24cm² 2: Area = 40m² 3: Area = 1400cm² or 14m² 4: Area = 800cm² or 8m² 5: Area = 2400cm² or 24m² 6: Area = 2400cm² or 24m²
47	1	Answers will vary.
	2	Answers will vary.
	3	37 cubes
	4a	A and D
	4b	12 cube units
48	1	Answers will vary.
	2	Answers will vary.
	3	Answers will vary.
49	1–3	Answers will vary, check children's accuracy.
50	1a	Right angle
	1b	Acute
	1c	Obtuse
	1d	Obtuse
	1e	Acute
	1f	Obtuse
	1g	Acute
	1h	Acute
	1i	Obtuse
51	1a	Acute
	1b	Acute
	1c	Obtuse
	1d	Right angle
	1e	Right angle
	1f	Obtuse
	1g	Acute
	1h	Obtuse
	2a	45°
	2b	90°
	2c	130°
52	1	a
	2	b
	3	a
	4	b

Page number	Question number	Answers
53	1	Check children's drawings.
	2	Check children's drawings.
	3	They are 90° or right angles
	4a	15°
	4b	5cm
	4c	10cm
54	1	
55	1	A (1,1) B (1,4) C (4,6) D (7,4) E (7,1)
	2–3	
56	1	15°C
	2	10°C
	3	London 13°C, Athens 28°C
	4	A line graph is used to show how something measurable changes over a period of time (or continuous data) such as temperature whereas a bar chart or a bar line graph is used to compare numbers of separate things (or discrete data) such as eye colour.
57	1	Approximately 25 litres
	2	13:45
	3	The driver may have stopped for lunch
	4	The driver filled up with petrol
	5	15 litres
58–59	1	3 hours 10 minutes or 190 minutes
	2	The 19:45 from Nottingham
	3	Answers will vary depending on which journey is chosen to work out the intervals from, for example: <table><tr><td>Liverpool Lime Street</td><td>12:00</td></tr><tr><td>Manchester Piccadilly</td><td>12:48 (48 minutes)</td></tr><tr><td>Stockport</td><td>13:02 (12 minutes)</td></tr><tr><td>Sheffield</td><td>14:09 (67 minutes)</td></tr><tr><td>Chesterfield</td><td>14:29 (20 minutes)</td></tr><tr><td>Nottingham</td><td>15:09 (40 minutes)</td></tr></table>
	4	Check children's answers for understanding of timetable (answers may vary based on which journey the child picks to base the extended service on): For example: a 14:48 b 15:15 c 15:45 d 16:25 e 17:00 f 16:51 g 21:20 h 22:16 i 22:10 j 22:30 k 23:12 l 23:23 m 00:11 n 21:30
	5	Check children's answers.